KING ARTHUR

AND THE KNIGHTS OF THE ROUND TABLE

KING ARTHUR
AND THE KNIGHTS OF THE ROUND TABLE

Howard Pyle

An imprint of Om Books International

Reprinted in 2013

An imprint of Om Books International

Corporate & Editorial Office
A-12, Sector 64, Noida 201 301
Uttar Pradesh, India
Phone: +91 120 477 4100
Email: editorial@ombooks.com
Website: www.ombooksinternational.com

Sales Office
4379/4B, Prakash House, Ansari Road
Darya Ganj, New Delhi 110 002, India
Phone: +91 11 2326 3363, 2326 5303
Fax: +91 11 2327 8091
Email: sales@ombooks.com
Website: www.ombooks.com

ISBN: 978-93-80070-88-9

Printed in India

10 9 8 7 6 5 4 3 2

Contents

Chapter One

How Arthur was Made King

King Uther Pendragon of the Island of Britain was dying. His land and people were being attacked and destroyed by Saxons. Somehow, the King had roused himself and bravely fought them at Verulam. The Saxons had turned back, but King Uther had lost all his strength and had collapsed.

The wise Wizard, Merlin, calmly sat by him. The King told Merlin of a dream in which a Red and a White Dragon fought with each other. First the White Dragon won, then the Red Dragon ... other smaller Red Dragons were conquered by the Red Dragon … till finally, the White Dragon returned … and the King had woken up.

When the King asked what it meant, Merlin answered, "It means that one of your people, the Red Dragon, shall drive out the Saxons. He will be famous all over!"

The relieved King slept deeply for three days. Many great lords and barons asked Merlin how the King was. They waited for the King to die soon. There was no heir, so each plotted to be King himself.

The next morning, the great barons and lords – King Lot of Orkney, King Uriens of Reged, King Mark of Tintagel, King Nentres of Garlot, Duke Cambenet of Loidis, King Brandegoris of Stranggore, King Morkant of Strathclyde, King Clariance of Northumberland, King Kador of Cornwall and King Idres of Silura, and many others, gathered around the King's bed. Merlin passed his hands above the King's face and he awoke.

"Lord," said Merlin, "Do you not wish your son, Arthur, to be your heir and the next King?"

The noblemen looked suspiciously at Merlin, for none had heard of the King's son, Arthur. The dying King whispered, "With God's blessing, I wish my son, Arthur, to take the throne. All those who follow me, must follow him." He then closed his eyes and died.

The King was buried honourably in the Roman church (now St. Paul's Cathedral). Everyone wondered who would be the next King. As Christmas drew near, the Archbishop of London asked all the great nobles to attend a great council.

On Christmas Day, the Lords and the common people gathered in a large, open field, near the Church. Prayers and Mass had started while it was still dark. A great, strange cry rang out in the churchyard. By the wall behind the high altar, there had appeared a huge, square stone. In the middle of it, there was a great steel wedge with a sword stuck in it with its point downwards. On

the blade was some writing in Latin. A clerk read it out: *Who so pulleth this sword out of this stone and wedge of steel is rightwise born King of all Britain.*

After the Mass was over, people ran to see the sword and the writing on it. King Lot, King Nentres of Garlot and all the Lords tried to pull the sword out, but none could move it.

The Archbishop declared that the stone would be covered with a tent, till the rightful King arrived. On New Year's Day, there would be a great tournament, which all the Lords would attend.

Sir Hector de Morven, a great Lord of the Isle of Thorney, with his son, Sir Kay and foster son, Arthur, rode towards the tournament. Sir Kay had forgotten his sword at home, so he asked Arthur to fetch it. Arthur rode back swiftly, but the house was shut; no one was there. So, he rode back and saw the dome of St. Paul's and thought of the sword in the stone.

Arthur found the churchyard empty. He grasped the handle and the sword slid out easily!

Without further thought, he rode back and delivered the sword to Sir Kay.

Sir Kay looked at the sword and the writing, and knew it was the sword of the stone. He showed it to his father and claimed he was the rightful King. Sir Hector knew the sword and marvelled, but he knew his son to be capable of lying. Then, all three rode to the Church. They went to the great stone. Sir Hector sternly told Sir Kay, "Now, swear on the Bible and tell me how you got this sword."

Sir Kay stammered out the truth. Sir Hector asked Arthur how he had got the sword. Arthur told him so, truthfully. He then put the sword back easily into the steel wedge. Neither Sir Hector nor Sir Kay could pull it out. Arthur pulled out the sword, effortlessly.

Sir Hector and Sir Kay realised that Arthur was the King and rightful owner of the sword. They kneeled and bowed before him. Arthur said, "I am astonished! Father! Brother! Why are you kneeling?"

"No, My Lord Arthur, I was never your father," said Sir Hector. "You are of higher blood than I thought. Merlin asked me to look after you when you were a week-old baby."

Arthur was sad to hear this, for he loved Sir Hector dearly. Then, seeing Sir Hector's anxiety, Arthur agreed to his request to make Sir Kay, the steward of all his lands.

Then, Sir Hector quickly informed the Archbishop about what had happened. The Archbishop called for a meeting of all the kings and barons on the Twelfth Day.

On the appointed day, all the men gathered in the churchyard of St. Paul's. The whole day, kings, princes and lords tried to pull the sword out from the stone. It did not move even slightly. Then, the Archbishop turned to Sir Hector and asked him to bring Arthur.

Arthur was a young man of medium height. He was dressed in a tunic of plain brown cloth and had curly hair and a noble face. The proud

nobles looked down at him, wondering who he was and why he was there.

The Archbishop called Arthur to him and said, "My son, I have heard a strange tale. Whether it is true or false, God shall decide. Now, draw the sword from the stone."

When Arthur grasped the sword handle, it seemed to fall into his hand. Many nobles objected that he was low-born and was not fit to be King. They complained there was magic afoot. Daggers were drawn, but Sir Hector, Sir Kay, Sir Bedevere, Sir Baudwin and Sir Ulfius, stood by Arthur.

The test was repeated thrice. By now, Arthur's life was in real danger, and Merlin advised that Sir Hector, Sir Kay, Sir Bedevere, Sir Baudwin and Sir Ulfius keep a close watch over him. On Pentecost, when Arthur pulled out the sword, as if plucking a flower, the enormous crowd cried, "Arthur shall be our King! We will no longer deny him!"

Arthur, thus, became King and the whole crowd kneeled before him. Even eleven of the

most powerful and ambitious lords, who hated him, were forced to kneel before him. Then the Archbishop blessed him and the King Kador of Cornwall made him a Knight. Arthur swore that he would be a true King and rule his subjects, justly and mercifully. The people were pleased, for they loved their new King. They believed he would keep them safe from war and troubles.

After Arthur received homage of all the lords and princes from the lands south of the Humber, he appointed his officers. Then, he travelled through his territories and met his subjects. He delivered justice where he could, and punished evil lords for wrongdoings. Arthur sent gifts to the six kings who had rebelled against him, but they rejected them. A tournament was held later, at which they clearly showed their dislike for him.

One night, there was an attempt to murder Arthur. The murderers—Sir Turquine, King Nentres, Duke Cambent, King Lot and Sir Caradoc fled, but were recognised. Merlin appeared and showed Arthur and his men a secret way to the

tower where the murderers were. Arthur and his men surprised and overcame them, but the main culprits escaped. The people of Caerlon heard the noise and came running to help their King.

A few days later, Merlin told King Arthur that his enemies were preparing to fight him. He ended saying, "Call your council, and wait for my return. Now, you must fight for your kingdom, O King, and for your very life."

Three days later, Merlin came with the news of an approaching civil war. The six Kings defeated at Caerlon had been joined by five other powerful lords, including a noble lord called Uriens. Arthur would find it difficult to overcome them easily, unless he allied with King Ban of Brittany and King Bors of Gaul.

This agreement was successfully concluded. In a few weeks, King Ban of Brittany and his brother, King Bors, crossed into Britain with five thousand good knights. With King Ban came his son, young Lancelot, who later became the most famous of all the Knights in King Arthur's court.

Later, just outside the Sherwood Forest, the scouts reported that the armies of the eleven kings were a few miles away. Merlin led King Arthur's army until they were near the enemy. Some men laid an ambush, while King Ban and King Bors hid in a hollow, thick with trees. That morning, there was a great battle. King Arthur, Sir Kay, Sir Baudwin, Sir Ulfius and Sir Bedevere performed marvellous military feats. They attacked six rebel Kings — King Lot, King Nentres, King Brandegoris, King Idres, King Uriens and King Agwisance, until they were wounded and unhorsed.

However, Arthur knew his army was not strong enough and thought of a plan. He sent a trusted messenger to the Kings Ban and Bors, who still lay in ambush. He then ordered his men to retreat in pretended fear and confusion. The enemy force, led by King Lot, pursued them headlong. The enemy was terrified when King Ban's and King Bor's men attacked, like angry bees from a hive. King Lot's men fought for dear life. As the evening drew on, the eleven kings

got together with their remaining knights. They vowed to die fighting. Then, they realised that Arthur had forced them upon a bluff overlooking a river. The only option to avoid the swords was to jump onto the rocks below.

Uriens laughed, "While we fought like wild boars, and only thought of killing, this low-born was clever. He played us like chessmen—first, an ambush and now, a cliff!" They waited and Arthur was angry with them, because they preferred death rather than being pardoned by a low-born.

King Ban explained to Arthur that they were excellent fighting men, and were doing what all brave men do. King Lot and the rest of the men decided to fight to death. Arthur gave the order to advance, but just then, Sir Kay brought a captured knight to the King. The knight said that the Saxons had landed and that all the eleven rebel kings' lands were threatened. Arthur realised that the Saxons would overrun his territory, too.

King Arthur commanded his army to retreat. At his command, the captured knight relayed

his message to King Uriens. Then, King Arthur offered to help them in driving out the Saxons. He offered them the choice of peace and friendship or loss of their lands and lives. All rebel kings accepted his offer, and swore loyalty to him. Merlin praised King Arthur for his wise action and said, "Arthur is the son of the noble King Uther and the lovely lady, Igraine of Lyonesse. He was hidden away at his birth as his life was in danger. Arthur is your rightful King."

Everyone, especially the eleven kings, were glad that they had a King so noble in birth and action as Arthur, the son of Uther Pendragon.

Chapter Two

Sir Balin and the Evil Dolorous Stroke

Once, King Arthur was badly wounded after a fight. Merlin, the Wizard, cured him and in a few days, they rode out together. Merlin led him through a strange, lonely and wild country, till they finally reached a lake.

The Wizard told him it was called the 'Lake of the Endless Waters'. In the centre of the lake, Arthur saw a great hand clothed in white, above the waves. It held a long two-handed sword in a rich scabbard. Then, a boat sailed towards them, in which sat a lovely, sad-looking lady, dressed in green.

"It is the Lady of the Lake," said Merlin. "If you speak well to her, and ask her, she will give you that sword."

The lady greeted King Arthur and he did likewise. Then he asked her for the sword.

"Sir King," said the lady, "that sword is mine. It is called Excalibur. While you keep the scabbard by your side, you shall lose no blood or be wounded badly. If you will give me a gift when I ask you, and will swear to give me back the sword when you are dying, then I shall let you have it." The King agreed to her conditions.

So, King Arthur rode up to the hand and took the sword by the handle. The fingers sank back into the water. King Arthur and Merlin rowed back and rode on to Camelot.

A few days later, a beautiful, richly dressed lady entered the council hall. She knelt at the King's feet and said, "O King, I ask for what you had promised. My mother, the Lady of the Lake has sent me."

"I remember," said Arthur, "and shall keep my promise."

The lady stood up and there was a great sword at her waist. "My Lord," said she, "this sword belonged to my loved one. An evil knight, Sir Garlon, killed him treacherously. I wish that my dear love be avenged by his own sword. My mother has given it magical powers. If there is a good and pure knight here, he can take this sword out of the scabbard."

The King and all the other knights tried but could not get the sword. Sir Balin took the sword by the scabbard, and drew it out easily.

"Truly," said the lady, "this is the best man, and he shall achieve many marvels. But now, gentle and courteous knight, give me the sword again."

"No, I will keep this sword," said Balin.

"You are not wise," said the lady, sorrowfully. "My mother sent the sword to find which knight was worthy enough to kill the evil knight. If you

keep the sword, you and the one you love most in this world, will face great danger."

"I shall take the adventure that is my destiny, good or evil," said Balin.

The lady wept and said, "I see you lying wounded and dying. I can't help you." She departed, and Balin also took leave of King Arthur.

Sir Balin searched far and wide for Sir Garlon, the evil knight, but in vain! Sir Balin returned to King Arthur and became one of his most valiant knights. Once, King Arthur was travelling with Sir Balin, when they met a knight, Sir Herlew and his sister. They were searching for an invisible knight, Sir Garlon, who had killed Herlew's lady love. Just then, a spear flew out of the forest and killed Sir Herlew. The lady kept the stem of the spear with which her brother was killed. Sir Balin promised her that he would take revenge.

After the knight was buried, Sir Balin and Sir Herlew's sister rode out the next day. One night, they stayed at the house of a rich knight, Sir Gwydion, whose son had also been killed

by Sir Garlon. Sir Balin also came to know that King Pellam, Sir Garlon's brother, was holding a great feast in twenty days' time. Sir Garlon would be there.

The next day, Sir Balin noticed that the land was very prosperous. Sir Gwydion told him that King Pellam had some holy relics that kept unhappiness, poverty and disease away from his kingdom.

Sir Balin went to the feast with the lady. There he found out that an evil magic protected Sir Garlon. He rode invisibly and no one knew who killed them. Sir Balin wondered what he could do. Very soon, Sir Garlon noticed Sir Balin looking at him, sternly. He flicked his glove across Sir Balin's face and said, "This shall make you remember me when you see me next."

Sir Balin, at once, drew his sword and cut off his head and thrust the spear stem into his body. King Pellam and the others were horrified and attacked Balin. There was a fight and

Sir Balin ran up the tower, looking for a weapon. Sir Balin used a spear that he found in the tower room and killed King Pellam with it. The castle walls collapsed and Balin fell unconscious.

Merlin rescued him and gave him back his sword and horse. Then he said, "You have killed King Pellam with the sword with which Lord Jesus was wounded. Now, the evil you did will end only when a pure knight shall come and get the Holy Grail. The relics are gone, so all is ruined in this land." People cursed Sir Balin and he was repentant.

Balin continued his journey and fought a valiant knight at a castle, as per the instructions of the Lady of the Castle. Both knights were severely wounded. Just when they were about to die they realised they were brothers, Sir Balin and Sir Balan. Sir Balin died first and Sir Balan died after midnight.

Merlin buried them in the green where they had fought. On their tomb was written in letters of gold: *Here lie Sir Balin and his brother,*

Sir Balan, who, unknowingly and most pitifully slew each other. Sir Balin caused the evil with the sad stroke. It has not ended yet.

Chapter Three

How Lancelot was
Made a Knight

When King Arthur was twenty-five years old,
his knights and barons advised him to marry.
He chose Guinevere, the beautiful and gracious
daughter of King Leodegrance of Cameliard.
When her father and Merlin arranged the
marriage, King Leodegrance said that he would
give Arthur the Round Table, which Uther
Pendragon had, in friendship, given to him
many years ago. King Leodegrance knew that
Arthur would appreciate the gift. A hundred or
so knights accompanied the Table. Originally,
a hundred and fifty knights sat at the Table.

When King Arthur heard that Guinevere was coming with the hundred knights bearing the Round Table with them, he was very pleased. He wanted their noble company more than great riches. He asked Merlin to gather another fifty knights, so that the noble company of the Round Table would be complete.

Now, around this time, King Ban, who had helped him in his fierce battle against the eleven kings, sent his young son, Lancelot to Arthur's court. He wanted Lancelot to become a great knight.

No one except Arthur knew who Lancelot was. Gawaine, the young son of King Lot, and nephew of the King, was also at the court. Both Lancelot and Gawaine were not as yet knighted, but spent much time together. Lancelot was the stronger and the better fighter; and Gawaine never won over him. However, they loved each other well.

Now Gawaine went to King Arthur and asked that he be knighted the same day as the King got married. The King agreed and asked

Lancelot what he would like. Lancelot said he would ask later.

The next day, an old woman came to King Arthur and said that Sir Caradoc of the Dolorous Tower in the Marsh was troubling her greatly. She demanded justice from King Arthur and asked if there was any knight who would punish Sir Caradoc.

Lancelot offered to go. Two days later, Lancelot came back with Sir Caradoc bound and red-faced, and said, "Now, Lord, I think Sir Caradoc would fight me, if you will give me knighthood."

Therewith, King Arthur knighted young Lancelot. The new knight and the battle-hardened Sir Caradoc had a fierce fight, but eventually Sir Lancelot won. King Arthur gave him Sir Caradoc's castle and lands.

Then, the King got married and there was much merry making and feasting.

Then, one day in June, Sir Lancelot rode into the fair green woods, looking for adventure. On the third day, when he slept under an apple-

tree, four high-born ladies rode by. One of them was Morgana le Fay, an evil witch. The others were the Queen of Northgales, the Queen of the Out-Isles and the Lady of the Marshes, who was Sir Caradoc's sister. She wanted to avenge her brother's death by torturing Sir Lancelot before killing him.

Morgana le Fay bewitched Sir Lancelot, who slept deeply. Then, the ladies picked him up and imprisoned him in a strange castle. When he awoke, he found himself on a straw bed.

At dawn, an old lady brought him some food. She revealed to him that her mistress, Morgana le Fay and the other three witch queens wanted to kill him. When Sir Lancelot heard that Sir Caradoc was the brother of the Lady of the Marshes, he realised he was doomed.

The old lady said that she would help Sir Lancelot, if he helped free her father. Sir Turquine, Caradoc's brother, had imprisoned him. Sir Lancelot agreed. Thus, late that night, the lady opened the door of his room and freed

him. She brought him his armour, his horse and took him to the Convent of White Nuns.

The next day, the lady led him to a forest. There, Sir Lancelot fought with Sir Turquine and killed him. He released all the prisoners and reunited the old lady with her father. Then, he left the place and rode into the forest. There, he met a wounded knight, Sir Meliot de Logres with his wife. The lady said, "My husband is a Knight of the Round Table. A witch once told me that a knight must bring the sword and a piece of the shroud from the Chapel Perilous. These would heal my husband's wounds."

Sir Lancelot promised to help and left for the Chapel. He reached the broken-down, lonely Chapel at night. Just as he reached, the ghosts of dead knights attacked him. Sir Lancelot prayed to God and succeeded in getting the sword and a piece of the shroud. Thus, he helped the lady save her husband.

When Sir Lancelot returned to Camelot, Merlin had told King Arthur of the knight's adventures.

The King made him one of the knights of the Round Table. Merlin said, "He shall be more famous than any knight now living. Yet he shall not be one of those three that shall achieve the Holy Grail."

Chapter Four

The Knight of the Kitchen

At the feast of Pentecost, King Arthur was holding his court of the Round Table at Wales. King Arthur never sat down to eat, until he had heard or seen some great marvel or adventure.

Sir Gawaine suddenly said, "Sire, you may eat now, for, here comes a strange adventure."

Two men entered, with a third, young man, leaning upon them. Once they reached the table, the leaning man raised himself; he was stronger and taller than those beside him.

"God bless you, O King!" said the young man. "I come to ask you for three gifts. One I will ask for now, the others, a year from now."

The knight asked for food, drink and lodgings for a year. The King agreed and asked him his name. The knight would not tell him. The King ordered Sir Kay, his steward, to treat the young man like a lord's son. Sir Kay was unhappy and made fun of him and his soft hands. He thought him to be a commoner and told him to live and serve in the kitchen, for a year. Sir Kay named him 'Beaumains'. Sir Lancelot and Sir Gawaine offered him better lodgings, dress and food, but he refused their kind offers.

The kitchen staff laughed at Beaumains, but he did all his work, readily and cheerfully. He was very keen to see the tournaments and was unbeaten at wrestling and other sports, amongst the kitchen staff.

Thus, a year passed and the feast of Pentecost was held in Wales. The King sat down to eat when he heard a lady had come with a strange adventure.

"Sir," said the lady, "my sister is famous for her beauty. An evil knight has kept her prisoner

in her own castle. You have the noblest knights in your court. They could fight the Red Knight of Reedlands."

The King said that until the lady revealed her name, none of the King's knights would go with her.

The lady was angry and looked about her, when Beaumains eagerly said, "Sir King! I ask for my gifts! First, please grant me this adventure that the lady suggests and then second that Sir Lancelot follow me and make me a knight when I shall want it."

The King agreed and said he would be knighted if Sir Lancelot thought it right. The lady was angry that a kitchen hand was sent for her aid and left the hall. Beaumains was given a good horse and arms. Wearing his new suit of armour, Beaumains took leave of King Arthur and asked Sir Lancelot to follow him.

Sir Kay tried to fight him, but was easily defeated. Then Sir Lancelot and Beaumains fought for an hour, until Sir Lancelot stopped the

fight. Sir Lancelot was surprised at Beaumains' strength and skill. Then, when Beaumains secretly told Sir Lancelot his real name, Sir Lancelot was happy to know the truth. He knighted him, but kept Beaumains' identity a secret.

Beaumains followed the lady, though she called him a coward and a kitchen servant. On the way, Beaumains overcame several wicked men and defeated two knights. Since the lady begged him, he did not kill them. He told them to be loyal to King Arthur. The lady was angered that she had been forced to beg him twice to spare the knights' lives.

They then came upon the castle of Sir Persaunt, a knight with five hundred men. The lady warned him to turn back. Beaumains told her, he would free her sister first. Beaumains also said that he was in King Arthur's court, merely to test his friends. The lady begged for his forgiveness. Sir Beaumains forgave her.

Eventually, Sir Persaunt and Beaumains fought. Again, the lady begged for Sir Persaunt's

life. Sir Beaumains agreed and a grateful Sir Persaunt promised him complete support. The lady revealed her name – Dame Linet. The Red Knight, whose lands came next, had troubled her sister, Dame Lyones for two years, hoping that Sir Lancelot or King Arthur would try to rescue her. Then, he would kill them, for he hated them.

They rode towards the land of the Red Knight. Sir Beaumains saw Lady Lyones at a window. He fell deeply in love with her and said that he would marry her.

The Red Knight declared, "She is my lady, and soon you will be dead!"

Both of them fought fiercely and Sir Beaumains cut off his head! The people in the castle cried out with joy. Beaumains ordered that the Red Knight's men should be loyal to King Arthur.

Beaumains was treated for his wounds, but he longed to see his lady-love. On the eleventh day, he went to the castle, but was not allowed entry. A knight, Lady Lyones' brother, said that they had to know his name and family name first.

Then Beaumains met his own brother, Sir Gaheris, sent by King Arthur to bring him home. It finally became known that Beaumains was actually Sir Gareth, the youngest son of the King of Orkney. Sir Gareth and Lady Lyones were married with great feasting and tournaments, at the court of King Arthur. Lady Linet was married to Sir Gaheris, for although she had a sharp tongue; she had a great and good heart, and was loved by all who knew her well.

Chapter Five

How Sir Tristram Kept His Word

King Arthur was called Emperor of Britain and its three islands. Nevertheless, most of the kings ruled over their own lands, but all offered their services to Arthur. They accepted his rule over them all.

The lands in Tintagel in Cornwall formed the kingdom of King Mark, who refused to pay his tribute to King Anguish of South Ireland. He asked King Anguish to send a knight to fight him.

King Anguish sent Sir Marhaus to fight. When King Mark saw him, he feared that he would have to part with his gold. Then, Sir Marhaus demanded the tribute, or that a knight should fight him. King Mark made a proclamation, asking someone to fight on his behalf, but no one came forward. Then Sir Marhaus sent his last message, saying he would depart in a day if King Mark's champion did not come forward.

Later that day, King Mark's nephew, Tristram from Lyones, offered to fight Sir Marhaus, if King Mark made him a knight. King Mark happily knighted him as 'Sir Tristram of Lyones'.

The fight was held on an island near Sir Marhaus' ship. When Sir Tristram was six spear-lengths from him, Sir Marhaus cried out, "Young knight, Sir Tristram, what are you doing here? I have great experience and you, none. I advise you to go back."

However, Sir Tristram was determined to fight and win a great name for himself. The fight began and they struck at each other strongly. They wounded each other, and Sir Marhaus sank to his knees with a deathly groan, when the sword went through his skull. He staggered away towards his ship, and it swiftly set sail.

Sir Tristram had also received a serious wound. The leeches, which sucked out diseased, old blood, failed to work on him. After two months, an old woman, who was called the 'Mother of the Mists,' came and examined him. She said that he could not be healed there, but if he went where the spear came from, he would be healed of this wound. However, he would receive a wound that would be incurable in his lifetime.

Thus, King Mark sent Sir Tristram to Ireland. Sir Tristram realised that he had defeated the King of Ireland's champion. Thus, to remain safe, he said he was Sir Tramor from Lyones.

Then, the King told him that Sir Marhaus had fought with a knight, Sir Tristram, on his behalf. Sir Marhaus had been wounded and had died two months ago. Sir Tristram pretended to be sorry.

The King ordered his daughter, the kind and gentle La Belle Isoude, the fairest in all of Ireland, to treat this knight's wounds. In a few weeks, her soft hands and knowledge of leech craft cured Sir Tristram's wounds. He became healthy and

strong again. Sir Tristram taught her to harp, and gave her costly presents. However, she valued his kind words and smiles more and loved him.

Meanwhile, a knight, Sir Palomides had recently arrived at King Anguish's court. He loved La Belle Isoude and declared he would become a Christian, if she cared for him. However, La Belle Isoude disliked and avoided him.

One day, King Anguish announced a tournament for unmarried knights. The prize would be the Lady of the Laundes, near cousin to the King.

Sir Palomides overthrew many knights, including Sir Gawaine, Sir Gaheris, King Morgant, the King of Scotland, and the Duke of Cambenet. Then a knight in white armour came, and the knights fought each other. The White Knight defeated him and made him promise that he would leave La Belle Isoude alone, or he would kill him. Sir Palomides agreed and ran away in shame.

Then the White Knight also went away, and none knew who he was. La Belle Isoude was relieved that Sir Tristram had won, and asked whether he had claimed the prize.

"No, I will not. I do not want to marry. I want my freedom to seek adventures," said Sir Tristram and went away. Thus, he did not see her tremble and nearly faint. For, La Belle Isoude herself was the Lady of the Laundes. The King and Queen and everyone else wondered who the White Knight was. Some even suspected Sir Tristram, but none dared ask him.

One day, the Queen noticed that Sir Tramor's sword was broken at its edge. She confirmed that it was the sword that killed Sir Marhaus. She told the King that Sir Tramor was the knight that killed Marhaus and wanted revenge.

Instead, the King decided to send Sir Tramor away, if he revealed who he was and why he killed Sir Marhaus. Tristram said, "I am the son of King Talloch of Lyones. I fought for King Mark, my uncle, for the sake of the tribute of Cornwall.

It was my first battle and I was knighted for it. King Marhaus was alive when he left me."

The King agreed that Tristram had behaved fairly, but that he would have to leave the country. Sir Tristram thanked him for his kindness and added that he would be his daughter's servant and knight and fight for her always, as long as he lived.

Then, Tristram returned to Tintagel in Cornwall. King Mark and all his barons were glad that Tristram was back again. He undertook several adventures and became very popular. Thus, King Mark began to envy and hate him. He wanted to destroy Sir Tristram.

The King called Sir Tristram, one day, and said that he wanted to wed the King of Ireland's daughter, La Belle Isoude. Sir Tristram was to be the messenger, but he was troubled because he realised he loved La Belle Isoude. The King did not really care for La Belle Isoude, but hoped that whilst in Ireland, Sir Tristram would be killed by Sir Marhaus' kin.

Sir Tristram set off for Ireland. Passing through the forest, he met a knight who was looking for him. The King of Ireland, Anguish, had been falsely accused and had been called to King Arthur's court at Camelot. He had requested that Sir Tristram be his champion. Sir Tristram agreed to fight for King Anguish.

On the day of King Anguish's trial at Camelot, King Kador of Cornwall and King Uriens of Reged were the judges. Sir Tristram came to know that Sir Blamor de Ganis, a great warrior and kin of Sir Lancelot was the opposing champion. Sir Tristram said that he would ask the King for a promise if he won the battle. King Anguish said he would gladly grant it. The fight began.

At the end of the fight, Sir Blamor was at the mercy of Sir Tristram. Sir Tristram refused to shame or kill the noble knight. Sir Blamor and his brother, Sir Bleobaris, made peace with King Anguish. Then, Sir Blamor and Sir Tristram embraced and swore friendship.

King Anguish and Sir Tristram sailed to Ireland. When the Queen and the kin of Sir Marhaus heard how Sir Tristram had conducted himself in the trial, they forgave him. La Belle Isoude was delighted to see him, but Sir Tristram hardly met her.

Then, one day, King Anguish asked Sir Tristram what gift he had wanted. With a lot of difficulty, Sir Tristram said, "My Uncle, King Mark, requests that you give him your daughter, La Belle Isoude. I shall take her to him, as I promised."

The King had wanted Sir Tristram to marry his daughter, and was unhappy at this proposal. La Belle Isoude was grieved to learn of it. The Queen feared that the marriage would be an unhappy one, and had a love potion specially prepared for King Mark and La Belle Isoude. She ordered Bragwaine, the maid, to give it to them in their wine. The maid gave the potion to La Belle Isoude and Sir Tristram. Both confessed their love for each other, and Sir Tristram promised to be her Knight and champion for life.

Sir Tristram took La Belle Isoude to the King. After his Uncle and La Belle Isoude were married, Sir Tristram said farewell to all in the court. He went to fight the pagans in the north. Seeing how sad Sir Tristram looked and how pale the Queen was, many men guessed the truth. For the love of Sir Tristram, none spoke of it.

Chapter Six

The Deeds of Sir Geraint

One day, King Arthur went hunting in the forest. His queen, Guinevere also went to see the hunting. She stayed back at the edge of the dark forest with Sir Geraint. At that time, a proud knight, a squire and a lady came that way. When Sir Geraint asked for the knight's name at the request of the Queen, the Squire whipped Sir Geraint in the mouth, and the three went away. Sir Geraint was angered at the insult to himself and the Queen. He went after them, promising that he would be avenged and would return the next evening.

He rode on, till he reached an old manor. There he saw an old man, who agreed to let him stay in his castle. They entered the hall and there were old rusted weapons everywhere, and ivy grew on the walls. A little later, he met the old man's wife and daughter. They all wore fine clothes that had become thin and tattered. The daughter, Enid, was lovely and smiled sweetly.

After eating, Sir Geraint found out that the manor, castle and all the lands had once belonged to the old man, Earl Inewl. His nephew fought with him and took away his castle and lands. The Earl had not handed him his properties, which he, the Earl, had held in safekeeping for him.

Sir Geraint also came to know that a tournament was to be held the next day. The prize was a gold falcon. He told the old man that he would fight to regain his possessions, and avenge the insult of his own Queen. However, he needed an armour. He also had to be with his lady-love to enter the tournament.

The old man said that he had the armour, and Sir Geraint asked to be his daughter's champion. Enid agreed, as she liked the young knight.

They rose early and by daybreak, they were in the meadow, where the tournament was to be held. The falcon of pure gold was placed upon a post, before the seat of the young Earl, Inewl's nephew.

Then, the knight whom Geraint had followed entered the field with his lady. He asked his lady to fetch the falcon. He proclaimed that his lady was the fairest and he would fight anyone who said otherwise. Sir Geraint challenged him saying his lady was fairer and so, he had a better claim.

They fought and Sir Geraint did well, even though his armour was rusty and gaping. After several lances were broken, the old man gave Sir Geraint a lance. He said that it was made by a wizard smith and had been given to him when he had been knighted. The lance had never failed him. Then Sir Geraint took the lance and felt strength pouring through his body. With renewed vigour, he hit his sword on the other knight's head. The sword cut through till the bone and

the other knight begged for mercy and repented his pride.

Sir Geraint asked the knight, who was Sir Edern of the Needlands, his lady and the squire to go to Queen Guinevere and do as she bid. Then, Sir Edern left with his lady and the squire for King Arthur's court.

Sir Geraint decided to stay with the old man. The young Earl then furnished the old Earl's manor for his comfort. He also returned the old Earl's possessions.

Before Sir Geraint left for King Arthur's court, Earl Inewl asked him to take his daughter as his wife. They were married at King Arthur's court and Enid was acclaimed as one of the three loveliest ladies in all of Britain.

A year later, Sir Geraint went home to Cornwall to his father, King Erbin. There was trouble in the land and the King was old and needed help. With Sir Geraint's coming, thereafter, men lived peacefully in the land, and on all the borders. Under the shadow of the strong young chief, no

border lords dared to invade the land and no fierce baron used oppression.

Geraint was so good at fighting that no one wanted to fight with him, so he grew lazy and stayed at home. He sat and played chess, or listened to songs and stories. Men began to make fun of him. The lawless lords became active on the borders again and he did not punish them. So, they became bolder.

When King Erbin heard about this, he was sad, and asked Enid if she was the reason for Geraint being so careless. The Queen was sad to hear this and hoped Geraint would change.

The next morning, when Enid awoke, she whispered close to the sleeping Geraint's ears, "Maybe, he is lazy and has lost all his strength and fame because of me." Geraint pretended to be sleeping, but heard her. He realised his mistake.

He turned to Enid and said, "Get dressed in some old clothes, get your horse and be ready to come with me." He bade farewell to his father.

Geraint said to Enid, "Ride ahead of me. Do not turn back or talk to me for any reason."

After riding for several days, they heard a lady weeping. When they went closer, she said, "O Sir Knight, please save my father. Four knights are demanding money and will kill him if he refuses. They say that our lord, Sir Geraint, sleeps all day and that they are our masters."

Geraint soon saw the four knights torturing a poor old man, who was tied to a post.

Geraint called out to the Knights, "Why are you doing this?" Without replying they attacked Geraint. He fought and defeated all four of them.

Then Sir Geraint took their armours, tied their horses and asked Enid to ride ahead of them. He said to Enid, "Do not say a word until I talk first."

The poor villager came to Sir Geraint, thanked him and asked him for his name. Sir Geraint said, "I am called Sir Slothful. If someone does this to you again, tell them that Sir Geraint will wake

up soon and they will face the consequences." Then he left.

Soon, they reached a wide valley and saw the fairest and richest in homesteads and farms that they had yet seen. Sir Geraint asked a knight who ruled the city. The knight said that King Erbin governed the city for King Griffith, also called the Little King. He also warned Geraint not to use the bridge, as he was poorly armed to face the strong Little King.

Sir Geraint continued towards the bridge. He saw a knight on a horse behind him, who said, "Don't you know if you carry weapons here, what will happen?"

"I come in peace, so why may I not carry my weapons?" asked Sir Geraint.

"When King Erbin's son, Sir Geraint, was powerful, he kept his borders clean of robbers. But now he is a sloth and I have to keep my people from thieves."

Sir Geraint said, "I will travel by this road, and fight you if you stop me."

He continued riding, and, on the way, he saw the Little King, Sir Griffith. They fought; though the Little King was fierce and powerful, Geraint defeated him.

King Griffith cried, "I have never fought such a brave and strong knight. Have mercy and spare me, and I will be loyal to you. Forgive me, I thought you had changed from a glorious knight to a soft fool."

Geraint said that he had not changed, and accepted his invitation to rest at his castle. On the third day, he ordered Enid to ride ahead with the other four horses.

On their way, they heard a woman crying. They came upon a dead Knight, and two horses, one with a woman's saddle upon it. Geraint saw three small dark shaggy trolls going up the hill with a Lady. He pursued them; they dropped the Lady and she ran away.

The trolls attacked Sir Geraint, but he fought hard and defeated them. Then, he fell down, lifeless. Enid shrieked and an Earl named Madoc

heard them. He took Geraint and Enid to his castle. Madoc was evil and wanted Geraint dead, so that he could marry Enid and acquire her lands.

Madoc forced Enid to eat with him. When she refused, he hit her and she screamed for help, but none dared come to rescue. Geraint revived when he heard her cries. He clutched his shield and sword and killed the Earl. The other knights ran away in fear.

Enid hugged Geraint happily and apologised for doubting his manhood. He apologised for forgetting his duty. They found a horse in the stable and rode out of the castle as fast as they could. Soon, they met the Little King, who had come to help them.

The Little King took Sir Geraint and Lady Enid with him. Physicians attended Geraint until he was quite well again. The fame of his adventures began to spread along the borders of his kingdom and reached his own court. When Sir Geraint and Lady Enid returned home, people gathered to welcome them. Henceforth, he reigned prosperously.

Chapter Seven

How Sir Perceval was Taught Chivalry

When King Arthur ruled over the Island of Britain, Earl Evroc held an earldom in the north under King Uriens. The Earl had seven sons; the last child, Perceval, was still a baby. Lord Evroc and his six elder sons were mighty warriors. But the brave knights of Logres and Alban killed them at Bamborough.

The Earl's wife was so grieved that she left her home. She took her little son, accompanied by a few ladies and boys, and went far away from war and death. She taught Perceval nobleness in thought, action and learning. He never saw a weapon or heard tales of knights and wars. He grew up with a strong body, fast feet and quick eyes and hands.

Every day, he practised throwing stones and sticks and had excellent aim. He could cut a sapling in one blow with a sharp stone.

Once, when their hunter was wounded, Perceval learned hunting from him. When his mother saw him returning with fresh meat, she was very angry and told him never to kill any living thing.

Next, he strayed deep in the woods. There, he met trolls and they became great friends. He visited them regularly and learnt sports and great wisdom from them.

One day, Perceval met three knights. The first knight asked him, "Have you seen a knight pass this way?'"

"I do not know what a knight is," answered Perceval.

The knight explained to him how a knight looked. Perceval told him that he had seen one, a few hours ago. When he reached home, he told his mother about the knights, and said he wished to be one. His mother was very upset and Perceval was sad to have hurt her. After some thought, she said, "Dear son, you are a knight's son. If you desire to be one, you may go."

"Yes, Mother," said Perceval. "I shall not be happy until I go."

"May God be with you! Go to the court of King Arthur and he will make you a knight. Protect the weak, poor and women. I shall pray for you!"

Perceval promised to remember all the nobleness she had taught him, and to return soon to see her. He travelled for two days and reached King Arthur's court. At the court, Tod and his wife, his troll-friends recognised him and saluted him. Sir Kay beat them for doing so. Perceval was angered to see this. He asked where King Arthur was.

Kay who was at the court told Perceval, "A knight insulted the Queen and took her goblet. If

you can kill him and recover the goblet, you may see King Arthur."

Perceval agreed and killed the knight with one of his sharply whittled sticks. When Sir Owen heard this, he was surprised that the boy had killed the knight. He gave Perceval the armour, weapons and horse that belonged to an unknown knight and asked him to come to see King Arthur.

Perceval refused to come to that court because Sir Kay had insulted his friends, the trolls. He asked Sir Owen to give the goblet to the Queen, promised to always be King Arthur's man and rode off. He sent many defeated knights to King Arthur's court to swear their loyalty to the King.

One stormy day, Perceval was at the doors of a ruined castle. It was the Castle of Weeds, the Lady there explained that it had belonged to her husband, Earl Mador. "When he slew Maelond, the eldest son of the great witch, Domna, she killed the Earl. Our daughter Anghgarad will

turn eighteen tomorrow and Domna will take her away."

Perceval was ready for Domna and defeated her easily. The witch said, "You must be Perceval, son of Evroc, because I am destined to be defeated only by you. You may come with us to the underworld, to learn the use of arms and about warfare."

Thus, Perceval spent a year in the underworld. When he was ready to leave Domna said, "You may take these arms and armour with you. If you fail to win the greater battle ahead of you, the Castle of Weeds and Anghgarad will be ours."

Perceval rode till he came to a ruined hermit's cell. He took off his armour and prayed there. His armour started shining with a white light and he saw the vision. It faded, but he wore the armour with a sense of wonder and rode towards Camelot, the court of King Arthur.

On his way, he came across a castle. He found that everyone inside was motionless. He saw a dazzling, white shield on the wall and picked it

up. Everyone woke up and the man on the high seat explained that he was King Marius. They had been put to sleep by God, till a good and pure knight would come. He gave Perceval the dazzling white shield, and said it would protect him in his battle against evil. Perceval left and as he turned, the castle disappeared.

Perceval slept in the forest that night. Before dawn, a voice spoke out of the darkness and said, "Fair White Knight, go to King Pellam's land in the north. Fight the evil power there."

After travelling north for seven days, Perceval reached King Pellam's land. It was now a ruined, lonely country. After Sir Balin had killed King Pellam with the spear, the Black Knight of the Dragon-shield had taken his place. The Dragon was alive and viciously burned all his enemies.

The knight was powerful, as he had also been trained by Domna. She had told Perceval about this, and he was ready. As they were fighting, Perceval felt weak and started praying to Christ. Gaining strength, he struck the Dragon that

turned on his master, the Black Knight, and burned him to death.

Perceval fell unconscious, and later, when he revived, he awoke to see Tod by him, who said, "We are at the Convent of White Nuns. I followed you and brought you here when you were hurt. I will go to your mother and tell her you are well and alive."

A nun came to serve him, and he recognised her to be Anghgarad. She was sorry that she had not thanked him for saving her. Then, after hearing of Perceval's great humility and purity, she repented her actions and became a nun. She said that he was destined to restore the Holy Grail to the kingdom.

When Perceval felt better, he rode to meet his mother. As he passed through the land, he saw that people had started living happily and the land was prospering again. People blessed him that he had ended the sorrow in the land of King Pellam.

Chapter Eight

How Sir Owen Won the Earldom of the Fountain

One day, King Arthur and his Queen were at Caerleon-upon-Usk. He was talking with Sir Owen, Sir Kay, Sir Conan and Sir Bedevere. Sir Conan was a brave, mighty knight. He narrated how he had got his horse, the beautiful Palfrey Bay.

"After defeating all the knights in this country, I went out seeking adventures that would make me famous. In my journey, I reached the Castle of Cover and met Sir Dewin, who told me of a great adventure. But, he also mocked me and said, I might lose this adventure. So, I decided to prove him wrong."

"I reached the fountain, and used my lance on the huge, chained cup, Sir Dewin had mentioned. Immediately, a thunderstorm struck and it began to hail. Somehow, I shielded my horse and myself. In a little while, I heard the birds chirping and a knight in sky-blue armour appeared. We fought and he struck me and killed my horse."

"I felt depressed and returned to Sir Dewin's castle, who gifted me the Palfrey Bay. It is very strange that no one else has faced this adventure, besides me."

Sir Owen decided to go to the Castle of Cover. When he reached there, he expressed his wish to fight the Knight of the Fountain. Sir Dewin laughed evilly, and showed him the way and told him what to do. Sir Owen reached there and struck the stone slab thrice. A troll came out and started fighting Sir Owen with an iron rod. Sir Owen fought a tough fight and defeated him. He decided not to kill the troll.

The troll said, "My name is Decet. You are a mighty knight, and since you have overpowered me, I will be your slave."

Then, he gave Sir Owen a dazzling blue stone on a silver string to wear around his neck and said, "This will help you make friends. Do not leave your love for more than a night and a day, or you will be in great trouble. You will be honoured and rewarded for your valour."

Sir Owen rode far and found the Knight of the Fountain and the Earl of Cadoc. He wounded the Earl severely, who rode back to his castle. Sir Owen followed him and met a maiden, Elined. She saw the blue stone shining on his chest and told him that it could make him invisible. She also helped him hide in the castle. In the meantime, the Earl of Cadoc died.

When Sir Owen saw the knight's sad widow, it made him very unhappy. He told Elined that he would wed the countess and take care of her, for the rest of his life. With Elined's help, he gained the goodwill of the countess and married her.

He also told her that he was responsible for Earl of Cadoc's death, but the countess did not mind that, as he took good care of her and the earldom.

Thereafter, several knights challenged Sir Owen, but he defeated them all. One day, he fought a mighty knight, who turned out to be his cousin, Sir Gawaine. Soon, King Arthur also arrived. Later, King Arthur took permission from the countess for Sir Owen to return to Camelot for three months.

Time passed and one day, a juggler saw Sir Owen's palm and sang a warning about leaving his lady-love for more than a night and a day. Sir Owen remembered the words of Decet, the troll, and rose instantly and left. He went seeking the City of Fountain, but he could not find it. He grew weak from misery and hopelessness.

A widowed lady, with her maids, came that way and rescued Sir Owen. After recovering, Sir Owen found out she was the Lady of the Moors and that her lands had been seized by the Earl of Arfog, who was forcing her to marry him.

Sir Owen felt sorry for the lady. He borrowed a saddled horse, armour and weapons from her, and fought with the Earl of Afrog. Sir Owen defeated him and made him return everything he had taken from the Lady of the Moors. Sir Owen told the lady about his wife and she gave him directions to the City of the Fountain. She warned him that the way was dangerous and full of thick forest, evil magic and only a brave and strong knight could pass through.

The first night, Sir Owen slept, a bear sat by him. The bear brought him meat when he was hungry and guided him throughout the journey. Then, one night, when Sir Owen prepared himself to sleep, a voice spoke from a big stone nearby. Sir Owen cried out, "If you are mortal, speak to me!"

A soft, sad voice replied, "I am Elined, imprisoned by Sir Dewin in this stone. The Land of the Fountain has also been made to vanish by evil spirits and magic. I used my magic to protect my lady and me, but it ends tonight. When the evil spirits come, burn them."

Sir Owen waited for the evil wizard-knight, Sir Derwin and his two sons. When they came, he killed them with the bear's help and burned them. Decet, the troll, was freed of the magic and appeared before them. He said that now Sir Owen would again be happy. Elined stepped out of the rock and then, they proceeded towards the Land of the Fountain. The Lady of the Fountain was overjoyed to see her husband back. Never again did Sir Owen leave his lady!

Chapter Nine

Sir Lancelot and the Fair Maid of Astolat

King Arthur made a proclamation of a great tournament to be held at Camelot, fifteen days after the Feast of the Assumption. Knights from far away gathered for the tournament, but the King was grieved, because, his most valiant knight, Sir Lancelot, had been wounded and could not join in.

The King left for Camelot for the tournament. Sir Lancelot was very sad and decided to see whether the physician, Morgana Todd, could give some medicine that would make him better in time for the tournament. When he reached Morgana Todd's house, he was told that he had also gone with the King.

Sir Lancelot turned back sadly, but the old man who opened the door, offered him help. He looked at the wound and declared that he was strong enough for the tournament. He warned him not to stay at Astolat, or else he would hurt someone there, and cause a lot of trouble.

Sir Lancelot said that he would not hurt anyone and set off. He reached Astolat and since it was night, he decided to stay outside the city to avoid trouble. Sir Bernard, the old Baron of a manor-house, offered him lodgings. At dinner, the Baron's youngest son, Sir Lavaine and daughter, Elaine, could not stop admiring him.

Sir Lancelot asked the Baron, if he had a shield that none recognised, which he could borrow for the tournament. The Baron willingly gave his eldest son, Sir Tirre's shield, as he himself was hurt and not able to ride.

Sir Lancelot thanked him for his kindness, but refused to reveal his identity when the Baron asked. He said, if he won the tournament, he would return and tell him his name. He also consented to keep a token given by Elaine — a red sleeve, embroidered with pearls. In return, he asked her to keep his shield in safekeeping. Elaine agreed happily, for she admired him, greatly.

Then, Sir Lancelot and young Sir Lavaine rode to Camelot. The town was crowded and the streets were full. The trumpets blew in the field where the tournament was to be held. King Arthur sat on a great, high platform, to judge who performed the best.

The knights formed two teams. One was the Arthur's band: among them were Sir Palomides, Sir Conn of Ireland, Sir Sagramore, Sir Kay, the seneschal, Sir Griflet, Sir Mordred, Sir Gallernon, and Sir Saffre, all the Knights of the Round Table. On the other side were the King of Northgales, the King of Swordlands, Sir Galahalt,

the Proud and other knights of the north. The tournament began.

Sir Lancelot joined the northern knights, as they were comparatively weaker. The northern knights were comforted, and wondered who this strange knight was. He overcame many Knights and King Arthur's knights decided to provoke two of the northern knights to fight, especially the one who wore the red sleeve.

King Arthur, too, wondered who the knight with the red sleeve was. Sir Lancelot easily won the tournament, though he was severely wounded by Sir Bor's spear thrust. When it was time to collect his prize, he said, "Fair lords, let me depart. I am victorious that is enough. Now, I would rather rest, than have all the wealth of the world."

He galloped away with Sir Lavaine, but in the forest he had to stop because of his wounds. A hermit cured his wound.

King Arthur and his men stopped at the Baron's lodge on their way back to London. There, Sir Gawaine met Sir Bernard. When Sir

Bernard learnt where they were returning from, he asked who won the tournament. Sir Gawaine started talking about the two knights; one with the white shield and one, with an embroidered red sleeve. On hearing this, Elaine flushed, for she had started loving the knight from the time she saw him. She brought the shield from her room and showed it to Sir Gawaine. Sir Gawaine recognised it and told them that it belonged to a brave and mighty knight. Chances of his return were small, as he was severely wounded.

Elaine set off immediately to look for Sir Lancelot and her brother. They found them in the hermit's hut after two days. Here, Elaine took loving care of Sir Lancelot. When Lancelot learnt that she was in love with him, he refused to wed her, as he did not feel the same. He took her to back to Sir Bernard's lodge and left for London.

Elaine was so grief-stricken that she did not eat, drink or sleep. She became very weak and died in ten days, after leaving instructions for her

burial. A letter was placed in Elaine's hand and her body was sent to London.

King Arthur read the letter out in his court. It read: 'Noble knight, Sir Lancelot, death has come to me. Though you did not love me, pray for my soul and bury me.'

Sir Lancelot was very sad to hear this. He did not love Elaine, but he felt sad at her death. He agreed to bury her in all richness and solemnity. On her tomb, in letters of gold, were set the words: *Here lies the body of Elaine, the Lily Maid of Astolat, who died of a passing great love.*

Chapter Ten

How the Three Good Knights Achieved the Holy Grail

Merlin had foretold that with King Arthur's rule, Britain would grow in strength and fame. Her knights would become braver and purer in word and deed, than the knights of any other land. However, after some time, they would become proud, and start using their strength for evil purposes.

That time had arrived and King Arthur's heart was heavy. He wrote down all his thoughts as a letter and sent it to his kinsman, Sir Brewis, to pass on to the old Archbishop, St. David. King

Arthur soon received a reply that three good knights would soon come to help him.

One day, Sir Kay entered the court, injured. Perceval had injured him, as he wanted to avenge the insult that Sir Kay had dealt his friend, Tod. King Arthur knighted Perceval. He knew in his heart that, he was one of the three good knights of whom St. David had spoken.

Sir Bors left Arthur's court, feeling that great adventures awaited him. However, while he travelled, he found no other shelter save an old desolate castle with broken, mossy walls. He stayed there for the night. As he lay, a spear with a blue flame appeared. Then, as he wondered, it flamed red and burnt him. Racked with pain, he could not sleep at all. The next morning, the great black oak door in the courtyard was spiked and bolted. There was no way out.

After three days, when he was weak with pain and hunger, another knight suddenly appeared. He attacked him wordlessly, but Sir Bors beat him well. Suddenly, his armour fell apart and Sir Bors

was horrified to realise he had battled a Demon. Then a great boar appeared. Sir Bors killed the boar too, but his strength was gone.

Sir Bors prayed to Christ and was ready to die. He slept well and awoke hungry, only to find hot milk and food before him. He realised that the evil spirits were trying to tempt him, so he stayed well away. By evening, however, he felt that he would die and prayed again.

Suddenly, an old man dressed in white appeared before him and praised Sir Bors for his patience. He blessed him and said that all his wounds would heal. Bors saw the Holy Grail in a vision and was healed. Then, he rode to King Arthur's court and told him about his adventure.

At Pentecost, there was a feast at the Round Table. When everyone was seated, the knights' name in golden letters appeared at every seat. Following their names, the surprised knights took their seats. There was one seat, where if a knight sat, he would be struck dead! This seat had these words: 'Sir Perilous. In the four hundredth and

fourth and fiftieth year after the passion of our Lord,' shall he that shall fill this seat come among you.' Today was that day and this knight was expected. Sir Bors and Sir Perceval's seats were on either side.

The door opened and an old man, who had helped Sir Bors, walked in with a young knight clad in red armour. The old man introduced him as Sir Galahad. He sat in the seat of Seige Perilous, but nothing happened to him.

Then, the old man told King Arthur that they should find the Holy Vessel to save their land. All the knights vowed to find the Holy Vessel and went their separate ways.

During his journey, Sir Galahad acquired a white shield, which could be used only by him. Sir Galahad fought against evil and helped the good knights. He ordered several knights to go to Sir Bedevere and Sir Uriens to help them push back the fierce pagans into their long black ships.

Sir Galahad and Sir Perceval freed Sir Bors from a group of other knights, and soon, were

on their way. The three ate together, related their adventures, and promised that they would never part till death.

They rode around the country doing what good they could, till they reached the castle of Earl Hernox. It had been taken over by the Saxons and traitorous knights. There was a fierce battle and the Saxons and the evil knights were killed.

The knights felt they had committed a great sin by killing so many pagans. They comforted themselves by saying, perhaps God had willed it. Then, an old priest came out from a secret chamber. He said, "You have destroyed the evil knights who plotted against this castle with the pagans. There are treasures here. By a prophecy I know that you are the three good knights who should achieve this deed."

Earl Hernox and his daughter returned to the castle. The castle was cleaned and all traces of battle were removed from everything. The three knights sat and talked; the doors and windows were shut. A great wind arose with a sad sound,

wailing and piping. Then, a great light shone in the middle of the hall. Through the light they saw a table of silver—on it was a silver dish.

Then the doors opened and they saw Angels entering with candles, a spear and a towel. They set the candles and the towel on the table, and the spear was placed beside the shining vessel.

An old man appeared, sitting at the table. On his robe, it was written in Latin: *Lo, I am Joseph, the first bishop of Christendom, who did take our Lord's body down from the cruel cross.*

The three marvelled, for Joseph of Arimathea had been dead more than four hundred years. He told them, "O knights, I am now a spirit, and have come to aid you."

He then said to Galahad, "Son, do you know that this is the Holy Vessel, Sangreal, out of which our Lord ate at the feast before He was betrayed to death?"

"No, I didn't know. It is what we have most desired to see, Holy Father," said Sir Galahad.

"It was brought here four hundred and fifty-five winters ago to keep Britain safe and prosperous. Too much evil and ruin has come upon this land, and the Sangreal cannot remain here in a doomed country. Tell no one about this. No one shall ever see this, for it leaves this land tonight," said the Bishop.

Galahad and Perceval were sorry to hear this. The Bishop said that the pure souls of Sir Galahad and Sir Perceval would accompany the Holy Vessel and him. Sir Bors, he said, would remain to fight for Christ.

Suddenly, a fierce light shone where they sat and blinded Sir Bors. When it had passed, he saw Sir Galahad and Sir Perceval still kneeling, with their hands lifted in prayer. The Holy Vessel, spear, and the Bishop were gone. The knights were dead and Sir Bors was sad that he would never see them again. With the help of Earl Hernox, he made arrangements for their burial.

He rode towards Camelot and told the court of King Arthur about the two brave knights.

The King commanded that the adventures of Sir Bors be written as history. Sir Bors did not reveal to anyone that Britain was doomed, because St. Joseph had told him not to tell it to any man.

Chapter Eleven

How Sir Lancelot Saved the Queen

After the quest for the Sangreal was completed, Sir Lancelot and Sir Bors were considered the most noble and courteous Knights of King Arthur's Round Table. The King's nephew, Sir Mordred, was jealous of them and sneered at Sir Lancelot, the Queen and Sir Bors. Sir Gawaine did not like the ways of Sir Mordred, his brother, and told him to stop speaking ill about them.

Sir Mordred was never cheerful, nor very friendly, and also spread terrible rumours about the Queen's personal knight, Sir Lancelot. He said that Lancelot was going to kill King Arthur and marry Guinevere.

Sir Pinel, a mean Knight and a friend of Sir Mordred, had first spoken wrong of Lancelot, Sir Bors and the Queen. Sir Gareth and Sir Brastias were worried that they spoke ill of the Queen and wondered what could be gained by it.

Once the Queen heard of these rumours, she decided to prove to the Round Table that she was not involved in any plot. So, she invited twenty-four knights to a dinner. She decided to appeal to their mercy, tell them that the evil rumours were falsely spread and how hurt she was.

Sir Gawaine loved the special kind of apples called Afal Coch. Everyone knew he ate them at dinner every day. The Queen had ordered these apples to be kept, especially for him. Sir Mordred decided to poison one apple, and removed all, but the poisoned apple from the basket. After dinner, the fruit basket went around the table, and the mean Sir Pinel took that apple to spite Sir Gawaine. Sir Mordred could not stop his friend

from eating the poisoned apple, as he would be revealed. So, Sir Pinel bit into the apple and died, screaming that he had been poisoned.

The knights were all ashamed, because they thought that the Queen had poisoned Pinel, since he was spreading rumours about her. Sir Mador held the apple in his hand and said, "Sir Pinel has lost his life because of this apple. The matter shall not end here, for I have lost a noble knight of my blood."

Sir Mador looked at the Queen in rage, and roared, "You are the murderess! I charge you with the murder of Sir Pinel."

The Queen trembled, and said, "My Lords and knights, I am innocent."

Sir Mordred sneered bitterly. King Arthur heard the commotion and came to see what was happening. Sir Gawaine said, "Sir, the Queen invited us to a feast with her. And one of the knights ate this apple, and is dead by poison. Therefore, I am afraid the Queen will be charged for murder."

King Arthur knew that Guinevere was not capable of doing this, but he had to imprison her. All the knights held her responsible, as it was her party. He ordered the Queen to be imprisoned for fifteen days. He said that a knight should fight Sir Mordred to help prove the Queen's innocence; otherwise she would be burnt alive.

The King was grieved and did not know what to do. Then the Queen sent for Sir Bors, and fell on her knees before him and said, "I beg you to save me from this dreadful situation. If my most faithful knight and friend, Sir Lancelot were here, I would have asked him."

Sir Bors said, "Madam, if I take this charge upon me, I will be called a traitor. Instead, I can help you by finding Sir Lancelot within fifteen days."

The Queen thanked Sir Bors and he left with his men to find Lancelot. After eleven days, they found Sir Lancelot in an old abbey. He was lying there, wounded in a fierce fight. Sir Bors told him what had happened and Sir Lancelot was so

angered to hear this that he immediately rode towards London.

While Sir Bors was away, Sir Mordred and Sir Agravaine plotted against him and spread the rumour that Sir Lancelot, Sir Bors and the Queen were together in the whole thing. They said that Bors had gone to warn Lancelot that it was the right time to strike. Many knights did not believe this, but many others were on Sir Mordred's side.

Sir Lancelot and Sir Bors reached London on the fourteenth day. Sir Lancelot was very enraged to see the noble Queen locked up in prison. He met the Queen and promised her to do all he could, to help prove her innocence.

At that time, the evil knights came knocking the prison door. They wanted to arrest Sir Lancelot and take him and the Queen to King Arthur, as traitors. Lancelot did not have his armour or shield, so he carefully opened the prison door so that only one knight could enter. He killed him with his sword and took his armour and shield. He fought with great

might and killed several knights, including Sir Agravaine.

Sir Lancelot and Sir Bors collected some good knights to help them. Sir Bors told them, "The most important task is to rescue the noble Queen. If not, it would be a shame for all of us." All the other knights agreed. In the castle, King Arthur was worried that Lancelot had not arrived.

Then, Sir Mador said, "Lord, the Queen has to be burnt, as there is no one to do combat on her behalf."

Sir Gawaine, Sir Gareth and Sir Gaheris requested that the King should send a messenger to get Sir Lancelot. Sir Mordred knew that if Lancelot came, he would prove that he was not a traitor. So, when the King sent a messenger, Mordred sent an evil knight to kill the messenger before he reached Sir Lancelot.

Now, as Sir Lancelot did not turn up at the court, Mordred made the King believe that Lancelot and the Queen were traitors. The King

ordered the execution of the Queen. He asked Sir Gawaine to carry out the execution.

"No, most noble Lord," replied the knight, sadly, "I will never do that. I will never stand by to see so noble a Queen meet a shameful death." Then the King commanded Sir Gawaine's brothers, Sir Gaheris and Sir Gareth to carry out the execution.

To this, Gareth said, "We will do what you command, but if someone tries to rescue the Queen, we will allow that."

The Queen was taken through the streets to be executed. Women were crying for the noble Queen. Suddenly, there was the sound of horses galloping — Sir Lancelot had arrived with his men. There was a short, fierce battle and many knights were dead, including Sir Gaheris and Sir Gareth. Sir Lancelot killed everyone that stood between him and the Queen.

He lifted the Queen onto his horse and took her to the castle of Joyous Gard. He said, "I will keep her safe, until I know that the King is assured of

our innocence. But our enemies have poisoned his mind, which is why he put the Queen to stake."

It was a mistake on Sir Lancelot's part; had he taken the Queen at once to the King, their innocence would have been proved. Now, though Sir Lancelot had saved the Queen, he had killed two good knights, Sir Gareth and Sir Gaheris, Sir Gawaine's brothers—this caused great sorrow and suffering.

Chapter Twelve

The War with Sir Lancelot

King Arthur and Sir Gawaine did not go to the execution ground, so were unaware of what had happened. The King was walking up and down in great grief, when a man dashed in and threw himself at his feet.

"My Lord," said the man, "Sir Lancelot has rescued the Queen from the fire and has taken her to some hiding-place. He had slain the brothers of Sir Gawaine, Sir Gaheris and Sir Gareth."

The King could not believe what he heard. Sir Lancelot had knighted Sir Gareth and loved him above all others. On hearing the news, Sir

Gawaine's face went pale. He rushed to the King and said, "Is it true that Sir Lancelot slew them both?"

"I have been told that in his fury, Sir Lancelot slew anyone that stood between him and the Queen," said the King.

Sir Gawaine cried, "They had no arms! Their hearts were with Lancelot and Gareth loved him as if he were his own brother. From this day on, I will seek Sir Lancelot and fight him until one of us is dead."

The King thought sadly that the best of his knights, Sir Lancelot, had caused the ruin of his fair kingdom. The company of the knights of the Round Table was shattered.

In the month of July, King Arthur camped outside the gates of Joyous Gard with his men, ready to strike. From the castle, the Queen could see that Arthur was very restless and sad. She went to Sir Lancelot, and said, "Sir Lancelot, if you make peace with my dear Lord, this dreadful war will be over. Something tells me that he is unhappy

to fight with you. You were his favourite knight. Please try to tell him, how others conspired against him and that we are innocent."

Sir Lancelot agreed and asked to speak to the King. When the King came, he said, "Most noble King, can we end this war? It is not of my making; I was only saving the noble Queen. How could you ever think for her to be burned?"

"She was charged with poisoning a knight who had accused her falsely. It was said that both of you were conspiring to kill me and to rule this kingdom."

Sir Lancelot took an oath immediately and said, "I swear it on my knighthood, and may death strike me now if I lie that neither I nor the Queen have ever had evil thoughts against you."

It was believed that if a man took a false oath, heavenly fire would instantly kill him. The moments passed and nothing happened. Sir Lancelot rejoiced in his heart to see that the King believed him.

Sir Gawaine came forth and said that the war would still be fought, because he was still angry with Lancelot, for killing his brothers. Sir Lancelot sadly said, "I will never forgive myself for that. I was mad in my rage and did not see them. I slew all that were between me and the Queen."

Sir Gawaine said, "Liar! You slew them to spite the King and me, because we let the Queen to go to the stake. We will battle against you!"

Though the King wanted to take back his Queen and call off the battle, Gawaine threatened to take the King prisoner, and fight.

The next morning, the war began. Sir Lancelot addressed his men and ordered them to save King Arthur from death or wounds, for the sake of their old friendship.

The battle was fierce. At one point, Sir Bors hurt the King without knowing who it was. Sir Lancelot rescued him and said, "I request in the name of Heaven, that we stop this battle. No one will gain honour from this. We are losing a lot of good men."

On hearing Lancelot's noble words, tears burst from the King's eyes and he ordered the battle to end for the day. The next morning, the battle started again. Sir Lancelot ensured that he did not hurt anyone from the King's side. Sir Gawaine and Sir Bors fought and Sir Bors was wounded. The knights on Lancelot's side persuaded him to start fighting. So, Sir Lancelot fought with all his strength and the King's side seemed dispirited.

In the evening, trumpets were blown and the war was called off for that day. King Geraint of Devon and the Bishop of London came to visit King Arthur. King Arthur was happy to see Geraint, because he was a noble knight, who refused to fight against Lancelot. However, Gawaine hated him.

"My Lord, I come with a command from his Holiness, the Pope. Stop this battle, take back your Queen and make peace with Lancelot. If not, this land will be doomed."

The King promised to do so. Gawaine threatened to join hands with the pagans and

win. Arthur sent a message to Lancelot, that he would make peace. The Bishop went to Joyous Gard and explained everything to Lancelot. Sir Lancelot replied that in five days, he would come to the King with Guinevere.

On the appointed day, Sir Lancelot rode into town with the Queen. Sir Lancelot kneeled and said, "By the Pope's commandment and yours, I have brought to you your Queen. I seek peace and goodwill between us."

With a fierce and dark look, Sir Gawaine said, "Lancelot, I shall never be at peace till one of us is killed, as you killed my brothers."

With tears in his eyes, Sir Lancelot said, "It was done in my madness. I made Sir Gareth a knight and loved him more than anyone else. The death of your two brothers will sorrow me forever. If it will please you, Sir Gawaine, I will walk in my shirt and barefoot into this town, and at every ten miles, where I find a holy house, I will pray for the souls of Sir Gareth and Sir Gaheris. That would do more good to their souls than the war on me!"

Sir Gawaine said, "You are safe now because of the Pope. But I shall only stay quiet for fifteen days. Then I will have your head. So get out of here as soon as you can!"

Sir Lancelot bent and kissed the Queen's hand, and said, "I have to leave now. Pray for me. If someone plots or tries to battle against you, send for me. I will always be there for you."

The King, the barons, the knights and the squires wept, and thought that Sir Gawaine had the most evil mind to refuse the noble words of Sir Lancelot. The King's heart was heavy.

Sir Owen of the Fountain said, "The pagans are stronger now, and evil has not ended yet."

Chapter Thirteen

The Death of King Arthur

Sir Lancelot and his men left Britain and went to Brittany, where he had a kingdom of his own. In Britain, the Saxons increased in strength and numbers. King Arthur was very busy fighting the pagans. In battles against pirates and the Picts and the Scots of Caledonia, he lost several brave knights, including the noble Geraint. Finally, the pagans, afraid of King Arthur's prowess, stopped invading Britain for a while.

Sir Gawaine still hated Sir Lancelot and persuaded the King to invade Brittany. First, the King would not listen, but finally he had to give in to Gawaine. Thus, King Arthur and his men passed the sea and attacked Sir Lancelot's country. Sir Gawaine's men burnt down houses and lands. Sir Lancelot did not want to raise arms against the King who had knighted him. The destruction they caused was so much that Sir Lunel of the Brake, Sir Magus of Pol and Sir Alan of the Stones, with his six mighty brothers forced Lancelot to go to the field and fight.

The battle started and Sir Lancelot's men were fighting, fiercely. Gawaine stood by the gate and said, "Where are you, traitor, Sir Lancelot? Are you hiding like a coward?"'

At these shameful words all his knights and kin persuaded Sir Lancelot to start fighting. So, the two brave knights fought with all their might. Sir Gawaine had a magic power, which had been endowed upon him at his birth by a great witch. The magic was that, from nine until noon, his body strength increased until it was three times his natural strength.

The two men fought twice and both times, Sir Lancelot wounded Gawaine badly. Though he had

the chance to kill him, he did not want to do it. He refused to kill Sir Gawaine, even though he knew that the former possessed a magical strength.

Meanwhile, Sir Bedevere brought the bad news from London that Mordred had imprisoned Guinevere. He also promised to give away wealth and land to any King who supported him against Arthur. King Arthur took all his army and left for Britain.

When they reached the shore of Dover, Mordred's men were ready to fight. They fought from boats and on horses in the shallow waters. Mordred's men could not stand the might of the King's men and fled inland. Sir Gawaine was badly wounded. The King was grieved that one of his most loved knights was about to die.

Sir Gawaine said, "I am sorry I caused you grief. I see now that I have been mad with rage against the noble Sir Lancelot, who slew my dear brothers, accidentally. Now I repent that. I wish I could live to repair the evil that I have done to you and Sir Lancelot. But my time has come. I shall not live till the evening…"

With the help of a priest, he wrote a letter to Lancelot asking for his forgiveness and died. Pirates killed the messenger who took the letter and the box with the letter was drowned. So, Lancelot knew nothing about Gawaine's death, his letter or Mordred's rebellion.

King Arthur believed that his evil deed of unjustly fighting with Lancelot had caused all these problems for him. He wondered why Lancelot did not forgive and love him now, since he did not come after seeing Gawaine's letter.

King Arthur's men were mightier and Mordred realised that he had to make his peace somehow. So, he sent a Bishop with his peace offer – a treaty. He asked for the Earldom of Kent and Andred, with a seat at London, during King Arthur's days, and to make him King after Arthur. The Bishop said, "For now that Sir Gawaine, Sir Gaheris and Sir Gareth are slain, he is the only nephew you have. If you grant these things he will be faithful to you and a strong arm against your enemies."

Both the armies, nonetheless, prepared for war. King Arthur and Mordred met each other to

discuss the treaty. They took a few chosen people with them. The others stood back at a distance and watched. If they were to see a sword taken out, they were going to attack.

When they were discussing the treaty, a viper bit one of King Arthur's chieftains and he took his sword out to kill it. The knights, who stood far away, saw only a sword blade upraised and thought that the battle had begun. They ran towards each other with their swords and spears. It turned out to be a very fierce battle.

At the end, only King Arthur and Sir Bedevere were alive. King Arthur killed Mordred, but himself was badly wounded on the head. The King felt that his end was near. He asked Bedevere to take his special sword, the Excalibur, and throw it in water. Sir Bedevere did not want to throw away such a noble shining sword, but the King persuaded him to do so. As soon as he threw it in the water, a great arm and hand come up through the waves. The hand caught the sword and vanished under the waves.

Sir Bedevere came back to King Arthur and told him what had happened. Then he carried the King and walked by the water, where he had thrown the sword. There was a barge there with some ladies dressed in black. One of them cried and said to the King, "Come to me, brother!"

"Put me into the barge," said the King to Bedevere, "for there, I shall have rest."

Sir Bedevere laid him in the barge and the ladies wept. Then, without sails or oars, the barge departed from the shore.

Meanwhile, Sir Lancelot learnt about all that had happened. He prayed for Sir Gawaine and was grieved at the loss of King Arthur. He said goodbye to Queen Guinevere and travelled west, till one day, he found a black barge by the shores of the Endless Waters. He stepped into it and was taken far, over the wide sea, until he reached a green valley and chapel.

Sir Lancelot went into the chapel and saw Sir Bedevere there. He was led to King Arthur's tomb. Sir Lancelot's heart burst with sorrow and

he prayed at the tomb. Within a year, Queen Guinevere died in her cell at Amesbury and was buried next to the King.

Sir Lancelot was grieved and he prayed and mourned day and night at the tomb. He ate very little and neither the Bishop nor Sir Bedevere could comfort him. At last, on a morning in June, he died and was buried at the feet of the King and Queen. His grave reads:

HERE LIES

SIR LANCELOT DU LAKE

WHO WAS CHIEF OF ALL CHRISTIAN KNIGHTS;

THE MOST COURTEOUS MAN AND THE TRUEST

FRIEND, THE MEEKEST DOER OF GREAT DEEDS,

AND THE GENTLEST TO ALL LADIES AND

WEAK CREATURES.

R.I.P.

About the Author

■ Howard Pyle

Howard Pyle was an American illustrator and author, primarily of books for young people. A native of Wilmington, Delaware, he spent the last year of his life in Florence, Italy.

In 1894, he began teaching illustration at the Drexel Institute of Art, Science and Industry (now Drexel University). After 1900, he founded his own school of art and illustration, named the Howard Pyle School of Illustration Art. The scholar Pitz later used the term Brandywine School for the illustration artists and Wyeth family artists of the Brandywine region, several of whom had studied with Pyle.

His 1883 classic publication *The Merry Adventures of Robin Hood* remains in print, and his other books, frequently with medieval European settings, include a four-volume set on King Arthur. He is also well known for his illustrations of pirates, and is credited with creating what has become the modern stereotype of pirate dress. He published his first novel, *Otto of the Silver Hand,* in 1888. He also illustrated historical and adventure stories for periodicals such as *Harper's Weekly* and *St. Nicholas Magazine.* His novel *Men of Iron* was adapted as the movie *The Black Shield of Falworth* (1954).

Pyle travelled to Florence, Italy in 1910 to study mural painting, and died there in 1911.

■ Characters

King Arthur: King Arthur was known for his Kingly leadership, his loving rule, and even his ruthless judgment of Lancelot and Guinevere (his wife). But often a very important part of Arthur's life is forgotten: his skills as a general and knight. He was a very able fighter and was well- versed in warfare.

Sir Lancelot: Lancelot was the son of King Ban of Benwick and Queen Elaine. He was the First Knight of the Round Table, and he never failed in gentleness, courtesy, or courage. Lancelot was also a knight who was very willing to serve others. He faced criticism when he saved the queen. But, he never turned his face away from his responsibility. After King Arthur's, he mourned and died near his tomb.

Sir Gawaine: Gawaine is generally said to be the nephew of Arthur. His parents were Lot of Orkney and Morgause (though his mother is said to be Anna in Geoffrey of Monmouth). Upon the death of Lot, he became the head of the Orkney clan, which includes in many sources his brothers Agravain, Gaheris, and Gareth, and his half-brother Mordred. He repented waging a war against Sir Lancelot, before his death and seeked to make amendments.

Sir Geraint: Geraint spent much time at King Arthur's Court, looking for action and adventure. It was during this period that he encountered the Sparrow Hawk Knight and came to marry Lady Enid of Caer-Teim (Cardiff).

Sir Gareth: Gareth was the youngest brother of Sir Gawain and the son of Lot and Morgause of Orkney. Gareth was an exemplar of chivalry who was knighted by and devoted to Sir Lancelot and who acted chivalrously towards Lynette despite her abuse of him.

Sir Kay: Sir Kay was the son of Ector (Ectorious) and the foster brother of King Arthur. Sir Kay at times had a volatile and cruel nature, but he was Arthur's seneschal and one of his most faithful companions.

Sir Tristram: Tristan, or Tristram in Old English, was a contemporary of King Arthur and a Knight of the Round Table. He was the nephew and champion of King Mark of Cornwall and the son of Meliodas, King of Lyoness. Tristan's mother died when he was born, and as a young man he took service with his uncle, Mark. He falls in love with La Belle Isoude, but refuses to marry her, as she belonged to his uncle.

Sir Perceval: Perceval was raised by his mother in ignorance of arms and courtesy. Perceval's natural prowess, however, led him to Arthur's court where he immediately set off in pursuit of a knight who had offended Guinevere.

■ Questions

Chapter 1
- *What was King Uther's dream? What interpretation of the dream was given by Merlin?*
- *What was written on the stone, on which the sword was stuck through?*
- *Who was able to pull out the sword in the stone?*

Chapter 2
- *Who was able to fulfill the lady's condition about the sword? What was he meant to do with it?*
- *What did Sir Balin end up doing for which he was cursed by the people?*

Chapter 3
- *Who did King Arthur marry?*
- *What was the 'round table', which was given by Merlin to Arthur?*
- *Who kidnapped Sir Lancelot and why?*
- *What did King Arthur say when he knighted Sir Lancelot?*

Chapter 4
- *Who did Beaumains want to rescue and why?*

Chapter 5
- *How did Sir Tristram wound himself?*
- *Who saved and cured Sir Traitram?*
- *Why did Sir Traitram refuse to marry La Belle Isoude?*

Chapter 6
- *Who did Sir Geraint marry?*
- *Why did Sir Geraint become a lazy lord? How did he finally realise his mistake?*

Chapter 7
- *Why did Perceval go to the underworld and with whom?*
- *Why did Perceval go to King Pellam's kingdom?*

Chapter 8

- *What did the troll give to Sir Owen and what condition did he place before him?*
- *How did Sir Owen rescue his wife back?*

Chapter 9

- *Why did Sir Lancelot turn away Elaine's love? How did she suffer from the rejection?*

Chapter 10

- *What was Holy Grail? Which knights undertook the journey to find it?*

Chapter 11

- *Who poisoned the apple in the basket and why?*
- *Who rescued the Queen?*

Chapter 12

- *Why was the King forced to wage a war against Sir Lancelot?*
- *Who forced Sir Lancelot to leave the kingdom and why?*

Chapter 13

- *Why did Sir Gawaine repent before dying?*
- *How did King Arthur die? How did it affect Sir Lancelot?*